my FAVOURITE ME

A FILL-IN-JOURNAL ALL ABOUT YOU!

Anna Brett

CARLTON BOOKS

How to Use This Journal

Don't live in a hand-me-down world of others' experiences — write about yours!

This journal is for you and about you! And the best thing is all you need to do is keep turning the pages for prompts, advice and great tips.

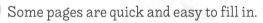

YOU CAN RECORD IT ALL HERE: your habits, your achievements, your well-being, your hopes and your fears. And at the end of it all you'll get a chance to see just how far you've come and what you've learnt about YOU!

There are various different styles of page in the journal, and some of the key ones have been listed here so you can use them as a contents list and flick back and forth. Note down any other pages that are important to you as you work through the book!

1. Some pages are quick and easy to fill in. Why not copy the ideas in a blank notebook so that you can write more later. For example:

2. You'll also find tracker pages. They are pages you'll visit again and again to keep track of your habits, exercise and moods, as well as your daily routine. You might choose to continue using these trackers if you want. For example:

3. Certain pages are packed with tips!
They are full of handy hints, and quizzes to
allow you to improve in areas where you might
need a bit of help. For example:

- 20—21 My Space
- 44—45 Yummy in my Tummy

4. The fourth page style you'll encounter
are those you'll want to look back on in
a week, a month or even several years'
time! These tell your story! For example:

- 10—11 Describe Me
- 36—37 My Future
- 66—67 The Playlists

My Cal

The year is yours!
What will you do with it?

Use this journal every day for an entire year! It doesn't matter where you start.

COLOUR IN YOUR SQUARES ACCORDING TO THIS KEY:

YELLOW = a normal day: you feel content

PINK = something brilliant happened today: you feel happy

RED = an important event happened today: something to remember

GREEN = you tried something new today: you've got a buzz

BLUE = something made you sad or angry today: you're down but tomorrow is a new day!

January

1	2	3	4	5	6	7
8	9	10	11	12	13	14
15	16	17	18	19	20	21
22	23	24	25	26	27	28
29	30	31				

February

1	2	3	4	5	6	7
8	9	10	11	12	13	14
15	16	17	18	19	20	21
22	23	24	25	26	27	28
29						

March

1	2	3	4	5	6	7
8	9	10	11	12	13	14
15	16	17	18	19	20	21
22	23	24	25	26	27	28
29	30	31				

April

1	2	3	4	5	6	7
8	9	10	11	12	13	14
15	16	17	18	19	20	21
22	23	24	25	26	27	28
29	30					

May

1	2	3	4	5	6	7
8	9	10	11	12	13	14
15	16	17	18	19	20	21
22	23	24	25	26	27	28
29	30	31				

June

1	2	3	4	5	6	7
8	9	10	11	12	13	14
15	16	17	18	19	20	21
22	23	24	25	26	27	28
29	30					

July

1	2	3	4	5	6	7
8	9	10	11	12	13	14
15	16	17	18	19	20	21
22	23	24	25	26	27	28
29	30	31				

August

1	2	3	4	5	6	7
8	9	10	11	12	13	14
15	16	17	18	19	20	21
22	23	24	25	26	27	28
29	30	31				

September

1	2	3	4	5	6	7
8	9	10	11	12	13	14
15	16	17	18	19	20	21
22	23	24	25	26	27	28
29	30					

October

1	2	3	4	5	6	7
8	9	10	11	12	13	14
15	16	17	18	19	20	21
22	23	24	25	26	27	28
29	30	31				

November

1	2	3	4	5	6	7
8	9	10	11	12	13	14
15	16	17	18	19	20	21
22	23	24	25	26	27	28
29	30					

December

1	2	3	4	5	6	7
8	9	10	11	12	13	14
15	16	17	18	19	20	21
22	23	24	25	26	27	28
29	30	31				

What was your favourite month of the year?

_ _ _ _ _ _ _ _ _ _ _ _

All About Me

"Be yourself — everyone else is already taken!" OSCAR WILDE

CONGRATULATIONS! There's a new film being released called *The Story of You*, and you've got the lead role!

Fill in this section with details about yourself and you'll find you've got the all the information about the star character right before your eyes.

The Story of You
CREDITS

Lead role (your name): Amelia Batty

Release date (of birth): 10/08/07

Producers (your parents or guardians): Caroline Smith
Richard Batty

Supporting cast (siblings and friends): Lucia & Charlotte
Batty. Harry & Sophie

Filmed on location (at home) in: Chalfont & GX

And in the school called: GX CofE

Key quote of *The Story of You*:

This Is me!

Check out your private, offline profile page –
the only person who can comment on it is YOU!

Choose your **THREE** favourite colours to fill in the rest of
your perfect profile in a super-stylish way.

HAIR COLOUR:

- ☑ blonde
- ☑ brown
- ☐ ginger
- ☐ black
- ☐ other

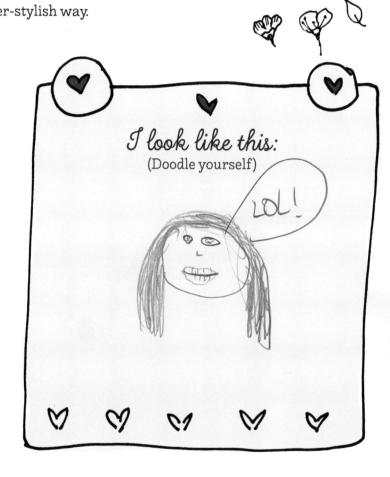

EYE COLOUR:

☑ blue ☐ brown ☐ green
☐ grey ☐ other: ....

Three words that describe me:

1. ....
2. ....
3. ....

Height:
- ☑ shorter than friends
- ☐ average among friends
- ☐ taller than friends

FAVOURITE COLOUR:
Rose gold / copper or turqoiuse / blue.

Favourite subject
at school:
F.c.t.

Today I Feel:
HAPPY   SAD
Relaxed
Anxious   HEALTHY
Athletic   Bored
CRAZY   Sassy

Favourite movie: Harry Potter
Favourite book: Scarlet & Ivy
Favourite place: my room / plane or a
Favourite song: Megan Trainor

I'D DESCRIBE
MY STYLE AS:
- ☐ sporty
- ☑ trendy
- ☑ geek-chic
- ☐ party
- ☐ laid-back
- ☐ other ....

9

Describe Me

Write your name here

....

and then write down the
words that best describe you.

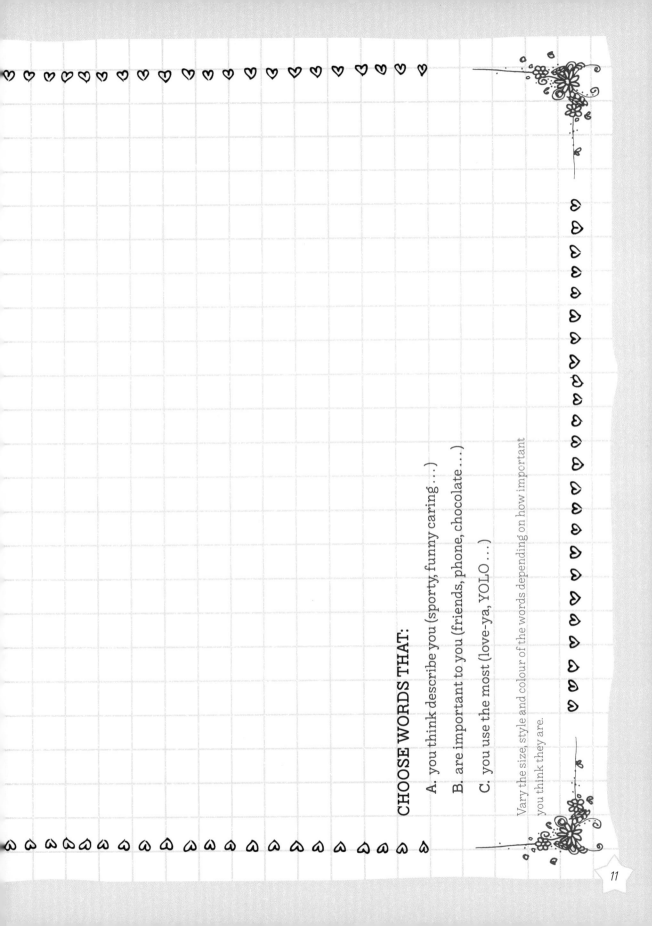

CHOOSE WORDS THAT:

A. you think describe you (sporty, funny, caring . . .)

B. are important to you (friends, phone, chocolate . . .)

C. you use the most (love-ya, YOLO . . .)

Vary the size, style and colour of the words depending on how important you think they are.

A Snapshot of Today

Today might turn out to be one of the best days of your life! Whatever happens you'll always have a reminder of this day with this paper memory you've created. You can do this at various points in your life and see how things change.

DATE:

M T W T F S S (CIRCLE THE DAY)

I woke up at
....

I wore ....
....
....
....

I WENT TO ....
....

I MET ....
....
....
....
....

Breakfast: ....
Lunch: ....
Dinner: ....
Snacks: ....

Best thing today:

. . . .

. . . .

. . . .

. . . .

. . . .

WORST THING TODAY:

. . . .

. . . .

. . . .

. . . .

. . . .

I WENT TO BED AT: . . . .

DONE AND DUSTED TODAY:

- . . . .
- . . . .
- . . . .

BEST BIT:

. . . .

. . . .

. . . .

. . . .

. . . .

. . . .

. . . .

Quote of the day: . . . .

. . . .

. . . .

. . . .

Routine Tracker

USE THIS GRID to track your habits over two weeks. Shade or write in the squares using a different colour for each line.

WEEK ONE	MON	TUES	WEDS	THURS	FRI	SAT	SUN	TOTALS
Wake-up time	7:30	7:23						
Slept for at least eight hours – Y or N?	Y	Y						
Portions of fruit and veg	5	4						
Glasses of water drunk	6	5						
Time watching TV	1hr	1.25hr						
Time chatting to friends	Alot	Alot						
Time doing homework	1hr	1.5hr						
Read a book – Y or N?	Y	Y						
Time spent outdoors – Y or N?	Y	N						
Helped someone – Y or N?	–	N						

Surprised by the results? Would you like to change anything next week?

"Every moment is a fresh beginning." – T. S. ELIOT

WEEK TWO	MON	TUES	WEDS	THURS	FRI	SAT	SUN	TOTALS
Wake-up time								
Slept for at least eight hours – Y or N?								
Portions of fruit and veg								
Glasses of water drunk								
Time watching TV								
Time chatting to friends								
Time doing homework								
Read a book – Y or N?								
Time spent outdoors – Y or N?								
Helped someone – Y or N?								

Did you achieve the change you wanted? How?..

15

Mix It Up

Which of your routines would you like to change? Pick one and create a grid telling yourself how to achieve it. If you wanted to get up earlier, for example, you could make yourself a list like the one below and try one method each day.

Now write down what you'd like to do differently and invent your own change chart.

1. Personal stylist – put your clothes out the night before

2. Motivate me – write down the thing you're most looking forward to tomorrow before you go to sleep

3. Change the tune – pick a different sound for your alarm clock or ask your Mum to wake you up with a tune.

HOW TO WAKE UP EARLIER AND GET GOING QUICKER...

4. Say no to the snooze – put your alarm clock on the other side of the room

5. Let there be light – open the curtains and let in the natural light

6. Drink it up – sip a glass of lemon water

7. Stretch sess – do five minutes of stretching as soon as you get out of bed

What worked for you?

Sleep Style

Deep sleep or restless dreams? Answer these questions to discover your sleep style and see what it means.

1 WHAT DO YOU WEAR TO GO TO BED?

A. Clean, fresh pyjamas

B. Whatever pyjamas you can find

C. That big baggy t-shirt you also wear around the house

2 WHAT IS YOUR BED LIKE WHEN YOU JUMP INTO IT?

A. Neatly made

B. Exactly as when I got out of it in the morning

C. Covered in books, technology, homework and clothes

3 HOW DO YOU FALL ASLEEP?

A. On your back

B. On your side

C. On your front

4 HOW DO YOU FEEL WHEN YOU WAKE UP?

D. Hey, it's a brand-new day!

E. OK, I guess

F. Oh no, is it that time already?

5 HOW OFTEN DO YOU WAKE UP IN THE NIGHT?

A. Never

B. Once

C. More than once

6 WHEN DO YOU FALL ASLEEP?

A. Roughly the same time each night

B. It depends what I've been doing

C. Whenever I feel like it

7 DO YOU LEAVE YOUR PHONE OR TABLET ON YOUR BEDSIDE TABLE?

A. No, I need my sleep!

B. Yes, but in silent mode

C. Yes, I don't want to miss anything

Mostly As = You're most likely a good sleeper because you don't let anything get in the way of your shut-eye time. You bed is saved for its one important job – helping you sleep! Don't go changing it.

Mostly Bs = You're not doing too badly, but you're sure to have a few difficult nights because you're not making sleep as enjoyable as it could be. Make your bed and treat yourself to some new pyjamas and you'll look forward to being able to go to bed.

Mostly Cs = Uh-oh, you're most probably a bad sleeper! Your bed is behaving more like a desk! Think of bedtime as different to the rest of the day and change your routine to match it.

Plan your ideal bedtime routine here and try to stick to it!

BEFORE BED I WILL: . . . .

MY BED WILL BE: . . . .

I WILL ALWAYS: . . . .

My Space

Whether you have a bedroom to yourself or share it, think about the space you have. Does it really reflect who you are... or is it who you were a year ago... or even worse, nothing to do with your personality at all?

List personal or decorative items in your space and review their purpose! Decide if you really need them or if you should chuck or upgrade them.

> Remember, it's fine to keep things you love, even if they don't have a purpose and you *don't* really, really need them!

ITEM	STORE	LOVE	FIX UP	DONATE
Old teddy bear		✓		
Shoes that don't fit				✓

ITEM	STORE	LOVE	FIX UP	DONATE

Ask your parents about donating things you don't use!

My Dream Room

Design dream it, then design do it! Doodle parts of your dream perfect bedroom on these pages. Imagine you can do anything you like! Then take a look at your ideas. Could you make some of them happen in real life? Then talk to your parents about what you could do to achieve it.

Choose

- Colours
- Work zone
- Relax zone
- Friend zone
- Beauty zone

Here is some help for how to design your room!

Key

Chair

Window

Desk

Bed

Door

Get on the Hobbyhorse

What do you love to do outside of school? Is it sport, craft, reading, singing? Here's a space to think about what you have done, what you do at the moment and what you dream of doing.

List all the activities you've done in the past couple of years. Underline the ones you really loved.

FUN WITH FRIENDS:

EXPRESSING MYSELF:

HELPING OTHERS:

Keeping active:

IN THE NEXT MONTH
I WILL TRY FOR THE
FIRST TIME:

In the next
year I want
to achieve:

WHEN I GROW UP I'D LOVE TO DO
THIS HOBBY AS PART OF MY JOB:

Spirit Animal

Whether you're a creature lover or not, everyone has an animal spirit inside them! Find yours and it will help guide you through life.

1 I'D SAY I'M:

A. Down-to-earth

B. Head in the clouds

C. Cool and calm

D. Hot-headed

2 I THINK I:

A. Am an easy listener

B. Think before I speak

C. Can talk to anyone

D. Am a chatterbox

3 DAY TO DAY:

A. I like routine

B. I never know what's next

C. I'm happy to go with the flow

D. I do what I want when I want

4 I'M MOST HAPPY WHEN:

A. I'm with my family

B. I'm on my own

C. I'm surrounded by my friends

D. I meet new people

5 I LIKE OTHERS TO:

A. Hug and support me

B. Let me have space

C. Help me experience new things

D. Not get in my way but follow me

6 A PERFECT DAY WOULD BE:

A. Games in the park

B. Reading my favourite book

C. Playing sport

D. Doing something new and creative

Mostly As = Bear

Having a bear as a spirit animal gives you **strength** and acts as a grounding force in your life. These big creatures give you **courage** to be who you are and you are great at offering **support** to others. They are social creatures, warm and **cuddly** and will always be there to keep you strong and focused.

Mostly Bs = Eagle

Having an eagle as a spirit animal means people will see you as **sensible** and **wise**. An eagle allows you to rise above any problems and think outside the box for solutions. Eagles are solitary creatures but that means they can react quickly to what is happening around them so your spirit eagle will be a great guide throughout your life.

Mostly Cs = Dolphin

Dolphin spirit animals are **playful**, **friendly** and allow you to be a great friend to others as you can always create **harmony** in a group. Dolphins pass on their energy to you and so you're likely to be good at **sports**. You'll always look on the bright side of life and not be afraid to try new things with a dolphin by your side.

Mostly Ds = Fox

The fox spirit animal is the **leader** of the pack and will help you to be a leader too. With a fox by your side, you can be wild and **unpredictable**, but people respect you as you go your own way and are very loyal. All this energy means lots of **creative** ideas will come your way.

How I will try to be more like my spirit animal in the future: . . . .

My Happy Month

A journal is the perfect place for you to think, feel, discover, expand, remember and dream.

Write down one or two sentences every day to record something that made you happy, something new you learnt or a great idea that you want to remember.

DATE   WHAT MADE YOU SMILE TODAY

My Year: Part One

Look back over the year that you've had and plan ahead. Think about your next six months on these pages and the six months after that on the next two pages. You can add important events, plans and goals – anything you like!

Write the name of the month at the top of each box and use them to plan, plot and dream. Goals could include:

- Volunteering during school holidays
- Cutting down on TV time
- Trying three new foods
- Making a new friend

My Year: Part Two

Return to these pages whenever you want to see if you've achieved your goals!

My Memories

"Things end. But memories last forever."

– **KUMAR MILAN**

Some memories, though, have a tendency to float away until something reminds you. Fill in these pages over the life of this journal.

Memories you want to make sure you always remember.

35

My Future

Where do you see yourself in 5 years, 10 years, 20 and 30 years? Write down whatever you most wish for and then set yourself on the path to achieve it!

In 5 years:

I'll be ...... years old
I will be ....
....
....

In 10 years:

I'll be ...... years old
I will be ....
....
....

In 20 years:

I'll be . . . . . . years old
I will be . . . .
. . . .
. . . .

In 30 years:

I'll be . . . . . .
years old
I will be . . . .
. . . .
. . . .
. . . .
. . . .
. . . .

SECTION 2

My Well-being

"Health is a state of body.
Wellness is a state of being." – J. STANFORD

This is all about your physical and mental
health — when you work on both you'll feel
your very best!

Positive thoughts

Positive vibes

Positive life

TODAY'S DATE:

ANSWER THESE QUESTIONS
using a scale of 1–10 (with 10 being the best)

- How healthy I think I am: ......
- How healthy I'd like to be: ......
- How fit I am: ......

- How fit I want to be: ......
- How happy I am: ......
- How happy I want to be: ......

The Power of Positivity

Whatever happens, try to see the **POSITIVE** in everything and you'll be a happier, more successful person!
You are what you think, not what others think of you.

> **IF YOU HAVE GOOD THOUGHTS THEY WILL SHINE OUT OF YOUR FACE LIKE SUNBEAMS AND YOU WILL ALWAYS LOOK LOVELY.** – *THE TWITS*, ROALD DAHL

YOU CAN EASILY TRAIN YOURSELF TO BE A POSITIVE PERSON.

Start by writing down three good things that happened today (they can be as big or small as you like):

1 _____

2 _____

3

Continue to do this at the end of every day!

What are you most looking forward to about tomorrow?

_____

_____

Think of a way you can be kind to someone and do it tomorrow!

TURN THAT FROWN UPSIDE DOWN.

Challenge yourself to turn that frown upside down when something bad happens. Here are three ways to tackle the blues.

1 Make a joke out of it. Laughter lightens most loads.

2 Treat yourself! Buy yourself a little present, spend some time with your friends and family, or plan a fun activity for the future. You'll feel better in no time!

3 Try to see the problem from the bright side. Could it lead to something more positive in the future?

YOUR MOOD TRACKER

Spend a month tracking your days! At the end of each day tick your mood, and what you did that day in the next columns. See if they match up!

MONTH _____

	WONDERFUL DAY	GOOD DAY	NORMAL DAY	BAD DAY	EXERCISE/ PLAYING SPORTS	FUN WITH FRIENDS	CHILL-OUT EVENING	EXAM
1								
2								
3								
4								
5								
6								
7								
8								
9								
10								
11								
12								
13								
14								
15								
16								
17								
18								
19								
20								
21								
22								
23								
24								
25								
26								
27								
28								
29								
30								
31								

Wonderful Words

"Let your smile change the world, but don't let the world change your smile."
– CONNOR FRANTA

A great way to help you be at your best is to surround yourself with motivational quotes. These will remind you that anything is possible and put a smile on your face!

When you're having trouble with friends:

"Spread love everywhere you go. Let no one ever come to you without leaving happier."

Mother Teresa

When you're feeling stuck with a problem you can't solve:

"Think left and think right and think low and think high. Oh, the thinks you can think up if only you try!"

Dr. Seuss

When you're worried about the future:

"We do not need magic to change the world. We carry all the power we need inside ourselves already."

J. K. Rowling

When you're feeling like school is a waste of time:

"One child, one teacher, one book, one pen can change the world."

Malala Yousafzai

When you're having a wardrobe crisis:

"Happiness and confidence are the prettiest things you can wear."

Taylor Swift

Ask your family and friends for their favourite positive messages and write them down here.
Try different styles of writing to make each quote stand out.

Keep a note of sayings that inspire you whenever you come across them.

Yummy in My Tummy

We all need food that tastes great and makes us feel good! Plan out your perfect food and drink line-up for a day.

Can you describe what it is that makes each bite great? It is that sweet taste, or maybe it's only delicious the way someone cooks it? Perhaps you prefer foods that are soft and squidgy, or maybe those that pack a crunch?

BREAKFAST I can't wait to wake my taste buds up with:

. . . .

Because . . . .

. . . .

LUNCH My favourite food for lunch is:

. . . .

Because . . . .

. . . .

DINNER I'd love to feast on:

. . . .

Because . . . .

. . . .

TREATS My naughty but nice treat to eat is:

. . . .

Because . . . .

. . . .

MY HEALTHY OPTION to gobble down when I'm having a break is:

. . . .

Because . . . .

. . . .

DRINKS Glug, glug, glug — the best thirst-quencher is:

. . . .

Because . . . .

Come Dine With Me

Imagine it's your birthday and you are having your nearest and dearest over for a special meal. What will be on the menu?

Menu

Upon arrival guests will be served this delicious drink:

. . . .

Canapés will be offered before dinner:

. . . .

The starter will be:

. . . .

For mains we'll have:

. . . .

♥ ♥ ♥ ♥ ♥ ♥ ♥ ♥ ♥ ♥ ♥ ♥

To finish, dessert will be:

. . . .

Throughout the evening these
drinks will be offered:

. . . .

♥ ♥ ♥ ♥ ♥ ♥ ♥ ♥ ♥ ♥ ♥ ♥

If people have space
for a late-night snack
they can enjoy:

. . . .

Move to the Beat!

It's a fact that exercising makes you feel better. It's time to get moving!

But rather than literally just jumping up and down on the spot (yawn!) grab a friend (or maybe your dog could watch!) and get some music playing. Plan fun ways of moving your body to different songs.

Let the music flow through your arms and legs and then write or draw down your routine here.

SONG   MOVES

SONG

MOVES

Listen to the beat and see if it's fast or slow, crazy or calm. Are parts of the song different to others? But don't overdo it with your moves! You're aiming to be a bit breathless by the end, but still able to chat to a friend/ the dog.

Gold Star

Award a gold star to your favourite dance!

Team Player or Solo Star

An easy way to get some more exercise in your life is to take up a sport. There are loads of things you can do as a team or an individual. Which squad will you join?

Answer these questions to guide you towards a new sport:

INDIVIDUAL

E.g. swimming, athletics, dance, cycling, gymnastics, horse riding, tennis.

Take up an individual sport and your efforts will lead directly to your success! Individual sports allow you to set the standard and just by practising you'll improve in no time. Achieving new personal bests is the greatest reward! But make sure you set yourself a schedule so you have to turn up to training just like you would with a team sport.

TEAM

E.g. netball, football, hockey, cheerleading, basketball, water polo, softball

Join a team and you'll make new friends just by turning up. It doesn't matter if you've never tried the sport before, just give it a go and your teammates will support you. Even if you're the worst player on the pitch, a team sport means you're still in with a chance of winning!

Do you like meeting new people?

NO → Do you like being in water?

YES → Try swimming or surfing

YES → Do you have good hand-eye coordination?

YES → Try netball or hockey

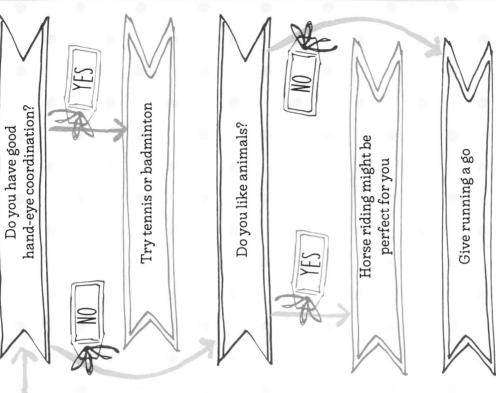

Do you have good hand-eye coordination?

YES → Try tennis or badminton

Do you like music?

NO → Cheerleading or dancing are ideal options

Do you like animals?

NO

YES → Horse riding might be perfect for you

Give running a go

Love being in water?

NO

YES → Water polo is a great team sport in the pool

Football might be best for you – it's easy to kick a ball

You'll end up following the sporting types around and moving your legs without even realising!

If you really hate the idea of sport, but want to be more active, what about learning to become an umpire, a 'ball fetcher' or a team physio?

Back to Basics

Imagine your great grandparents (bonus points if you know their names!) **when they were your age.**

Think of some of the things they might have done, then see if you can get back to basics and experience them all in a week. Then fill in the family tree below.

Here are some to get you started. Tick them off once you've completed them. How many did you really enjoy? Continue to include them in your regular daily routine!

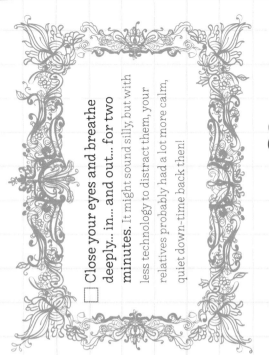

☐ Close your eyes and breathe deeply... in... and out... for two minutes. It might sound silly, but with less technology to distract them, your relatives probably had a lot more calm, quiet down-time back then!

☐ Drink a glass of lemon water. There weren't many options other than water and milk for children to drink back in the old days, so see if you can get back to basics for a week.

☐ Sit outside for ten minutes and do nothing – no phone, no talking, no worrying – just enjoy the natural world. Over 200 years ago the world had no TV or computers to keep people indoors. Your relatives would have probably spent more time outdoors than you do!

☐ Eat something you've grown yourself rather than purchased from a shop. Where did the food you ate today come from? The supermarket? Decades ago your grandparents would have waited months to eat certain things that they had grown!

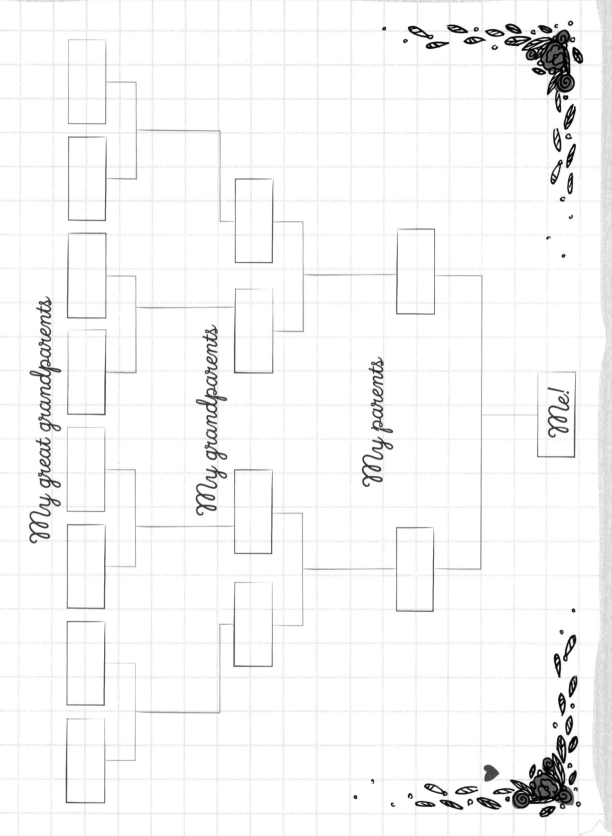

My great grandparents

My grandparents

My parents

Me!

Get Your Stretch On

Ever wondered why cats and dogs stretch so much? Because it feels sooo good! Give this stretch routine a go and you'll be purring like a cat in no time.

Only hold poses for as long as is comfortable – just feel a gentle stretch, and don't force anything – and move slowly and thoughtfully. The more you do it, the easier it'll become.

Firstly, find somewhere with plenty of room to stretch out and check with an adult that it's OK to use the space. Don't do this routine just after you have eaten.

1. Stand with your feet touching and arms down by your side. Breathe deeply and then slowly raise your arms up to the sky.

2. Take a deep breath then exhale slowly and bend forward to touch your toes. It's OK if you need to bend your knees a little.

3. Lift your right leg up and take a step back, away from your body. Place your hands flat on the floor.

4. Bring your left leg back to line up with the right. Keeping your hands on the floor, lift your hips up to create an upside-down V shape with your body. Hold for ten seconds, or for as long as is comfortable.

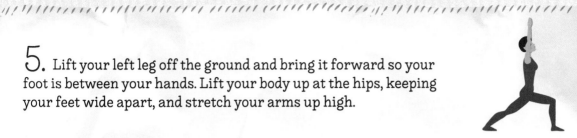

5. Lift your left leg off the ground and bring it forward so your foot is between your hands. Lift your body up at the hips, keeping your feet wide apart, and stretch your arms up high.

6. Twist your body and back foot to the right and point your left hand forward over your left leg and your right hand backwards over your right leg. Look forward and hold for ten seconds.

7. Twist your body and back foot to face forward, then raise both arms above your head and point your fingertips up to the sky. Breathe deeply and count to ten.

8. Bring both hands down to the ground, place them either side of your left foot, shoulder-width apart. Move your left leg back and then bring your body down to lay flat on the floor.

9. Bend the top half of your body up, your weight pressing down through your hands.

10. Lower yourself gently back down into a flat position, then lift your hips to the sky and flex your feet forward again so you take up the upside-down V pose.

11. Shuffle your hands back towards your feet and then slowly lift your upper body up until you are back in a standing position. Stand perfectly still for ten seconds and concentrate on your breathing. Hopefully it feels like you've given your body a good cat-stretch!

My Perfect Chill Evening

Tune out. Turn off. Take some time to relax. Allow your body and mind to switch off and chill out every now and then with an evening of "you time".

1 WHAT ARE YOUR FAVOURITE WAYS TO RELAX?

Make a list of your top "you time" activities.

_____

_____

_____

_____

_____

Here are a couple more ideas. Tick the ones you enjoy.

- [ ] DIY manicure
- [ ] face mask
- [ ] watching a funny movie
- [ ] bubble bath
- [ ] reading a book

2 PLAN IT

Now schedule in your next chill-out evening. Write the day and date of your next chill-out evening here:

_____

_____

Take time to prepare your evening, and make sure you don't plan too much.
Pick three activities from your "you time" list you'd like to do.

1 _____

2 _____

3 _____

3 TOP TIPS

1 Tell family and friends about your evening to make sure they **don't interrupt you.**

2 Pick a song or poem that makes you feel good and play or read this at the start of your relax time. It'll get your head in the zone!

3 Try having some no-screen time at the start or end of your evening, and switch off your phone.

4 PREP YOUR CHILL ZONE

Before you start your perfect chill-out evening have a quick tidy up to make the space around you cosy and calming, with no harsh lights or too much clutter. Make a list of everything you'll need to help you chill and gather it together in advance.

Here are a few more ideas for your chill area. Tick the objects you'd like to have ready.

- **candles** (never leave a candle unattended and make sure to ask a grownup before you light one!)

- **relaxing music** (have a look on pages 66–67 to find your playlists)

- a **cosy blanket**

- a cup of **herbal tea**

1

2

3

4

5

Heaven Scents

Don't you just love the smell of freshly cut grass? What about coming home to cookies straight out of the oven? There are so many amazing smells – write down the ones you love here.

LIP BALM IN THIS FLAVOUR SMELLS THE BEST:

....

Do you prefer the smell of sun lotion or cooling moisturizer:

....

THE BEST-SMELLING BUBBLE BATH IS:

....

MY FAVE shampoo SMELL IS:

....

MY FAVOURITE SMELL AT SCHOOL IS:

My favourite
COOKING SMELL IS:
. . . .

MY FAVOURITE FRUIT SMELL IS:
. . . .

Flowers that smell
the strongest are:
. . . .

59

Nifty Nails and Lovely Lips

It's fun and easy to look after your nails and lips and you can show off your personality by what you wear on them too!

Lips in sync

Here are some top tips for lushious lips!

1. Gently rub yur lips with a toothbrush to exfoliate.

2. Use lip balm to protect them from getting dry.

3. Apply lip balm within the natural shape of your lips. Don't smear it all over your skin too.

4. Pick a lip gloss colour that suits your skin tone.

5. Go for a lipstick in your fave colour for a fun look on the weekend.

6. Pick a product with a juicy smell to make those lips smile!

LIP BALM IS SOOTHING AND SCENTED.

LIP GLOSS WILL ADD SOME SHINE.

LIPSTICK IS THERE TO CREATE A COLOUR POP.

Nurture your nails

Look after your nails — you have to look at them every day after all!

1. Don't bite or chew them!

2. Moisturise your hands, fingers and cuticles.

3. Keep them filed so you don't catch your clothes on sharp, jagged edges. Only file in one direction, though.

4. Nails are always growing so you can have fun and create different shapes and lengths to match your mood each week.

5. Apply a clear polish before adding bright varnish to stop any staining.

6. Create nail art by using a second colour, and applying glitter or using stickers.

WHICH OF THESE COLOURS ARE YOUR FAVOURITE?

SMEAR A BLOB OF YOUR FAVOURITE LIP PRODUCTS HERE AND MAKE NOTES ABOUT THEM.

Cosy on Up

You know that feeling you get when it's cold and rainy outside and you're snuggled inside on the sofa with a blanket, a candle and a hot chocolate? Your body and mind are happy and at ease. Ahhhh....

But there doesn't always have to be terrible weather outside to get that great feeling inside!

Plan to cosy on up for an hour, and prep according to these four areas:

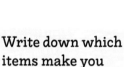

1. ATMOSPHERE

Turn off that overhead light and use lamps and fairy lights to set the mood. Put on some chilled-out music in the background and grab a book or magazine to read. If you can, spray some calming scents around the room. Lavender, cinnamon and vanilla are great, or just pick some fresh flowers and put them in a vase near you.

Write down which items make you feel relaxed:

- . . . .
- . . . .
- . . . .

2. ENJOY THE MOMENT

A key part of feeling cosy is being present in the moment. This means no technology to distract you – turn that phone off! Set yourself a period of time where you promise not to think about school, homework, exams or gossip. Just enjoy the moment.

I'm going to switch my phone off for this amount of time during my cosy hour:

. . . .

3. COMFORT

One of the best bits about feeling cosy is getting comfortable. Put on your fluffy pyjamas, wrap up in a cosy blanket, slip on some knitted socks, grab your favourite cuddly toy and you'll have ticked the comfort box. Give your insides some comfort too with your favourite sweet treats and a hot drink.

Comfort items collected for my cosy hour:

- . . . .
- . . . .
- . . . .

4. HAPPY AND GRATEFUL

Being thankful for what you have and forgetting any arguments or annoyances is the final part of feeling cosy and relaxed. There's a time and a place to be competitive, argumentative or wishing things could change – but it's not now! Enjoy your home and knowing your friends and family are around you.

Things I am grateful for:

- . . . .
- . . . .
- . . . .

63

She Loves to Read

Do you love to read? Fill in the spines of these books to complete the library of your dreams!

MY FAVOURITE BOOKS

BOOKS TO READ

BOOKS FOR SCHOOL

MAYBE SOMEDAY...

FACTUAL BOOKS TO READ

"You can find magic wherever you look.
Sit back and relax, all you need is a book."

– DR. SEUSS

The Playlists

Make sure you have a special soundtrack for whatever each day brings. Write down your favourite songs in each category!

You can now start to use this as a music diary. Every time you hear a new song that you love, make a note of it here along with the date.

Party: Date:

Relax: Date:

Happy: Date:

My favourite song today:

Angry: **Date:**

Motivation: **Date:**

Study: **Date:**

Fitness: **Date:**

Give a Little

Spread some joy by giving to others. Write down ways you can put a smile on someone else's face and it is sure to make you smile too!

WRITE DOWN THREE WAYS THAT YOU CAN HELP THOSE WHO ARE IN NEED

1

2

3

WRITE DOWN THREE WAYS YOU CAN HELP MAKE PEOPLE AT HOME SMILE

1

2

3

WRITE DOWN THREE WAYS YOU CAN BRING HAPPINESS TO PEOPLE AT SCHOOL

1 _____

2 _____

3 _____

WRITE DOWN WHEN SOMEONE DOES SOMETHING THAT PUTS
A SMILE ON YOUR FACE AND THEN THANK THEM FOR IT

1 _____

2 _____

3 _____

WRITE A LIST OF TEN PEOPLE YOU ARE GRATEFUL FOR IN YOUR LIFE — THEN TELL THEM!

1 _____   6 _____

2 _____   7 _____

3 _____   8 _____

4 _____   9 _____

5 _____   10 _____

Mood Tracker

Track your moods and feelings for the next four weeks. Draw in an emoji face to show how you felt at each stage of the day. Then write a sentence about each day but focus on different things for the four weeks.

WEEK ONE	TODAY I FELT		MORNING	MIDDAY	AFTERNOON	EVENING
Monday						
Tuesday						
Wednesday						
Thursday						
Friday						
Saturday						
Sunday						

WEEK TWO	MOST LOOKING FORWARD TO		MORNING	MIDDAY	AFTERNOON	EVENING
Monday						
Tuesday						
Wednesday						
Thursday						
Friday						
Saturday						
Sunday						

> " THE PURPOSE OF LIFE IS TO BE HAPPY. "   — DALAI LAMA

WEEK THREE	BEST THING	MORNING	MIDDAY	AFTERNOON	EVENING
Monday					
Tuesday					
Wednesday					
Thursday					
Friday					
Saturday					
Sunday					

WEEK FOUR	I'M GRATEFUL FOR	MORNING	MIDDAY	AFTERNOON	EVENING
Monday					
Tuesday					
Wednesday					
Thursday					
Friday					
Saturday					
Sunday					

Doodle Delights

Every time you feel sad, worried or angry, imagine all your concerns are trapped inside one of these circles and turn them into something happy – a shining sun, a smiley face, a gold medal, a flower – whatever you want!

When you turn back to these pages you won't remember the bad things inside the circle, you'll just see happy doodles.

" You can't have a rainbow without a little rain!" – ANON

Dreaming Big

"If you can dream it, you can do it."
— WALT DISNEY

The future is yours for the taking — believe that you can do whatever you set out to achieve!

In this section, you should take the time to review your achievements to date, and set yourself some goals for the coming year that will allow you to take a few steps towards your dream!

In the future I'd love to:

My dream job is:

....

My dream holiday is:

....

My dream home would be:

....

My favourite item to carry with me everywhere would be:

....

Dream Daze

What you dream about when you're asleep might give you clues to your deepest wishes and worries. Or might make no sense at all!

Track your dreams here...

DATE	DREAM	WHAT I THINK IT MEANS

DATE	DREAM	WHAT I THINK IT MEANS

"In dreams we enter a world that's entirely our own."

– ALBUS DUMBLEDORE
in *Harry Potter and the Prisoner of Azkaban*. J. K. Rowling.

Welcome to the Year 20__!

Plan your life five years from now! Where would you like to be? Who will be your friends? What are your goals? Dream ahead and write it all down here.

WHAT WILL MY STYLE BE LIKE?

WILL I HAVE A SPECIAL PERSON IN MY LIFE?

HOW WILL I RELAX?

WHAT WILL
I DO FOR FUN?

WHAT WILL MY
ROOM LOOK LIKE?

WHAT WILL BE MY SPECIAL
GOALS FOR THE FUTURE?

WHO ARE GOING TO
BE MY FRIENDS?

New Day Resolutions

Never mind waiting until the new year to make your resolutions. If you want to achieve your dreams, then you should put yourself on the path to achieve them now!

My resolutions

TOMORROW:

1
2
3

NEXT WEEK:

1
2
3

NEXT MONTH:

1
2
3

THIS YEAR:

1 _____
2 _____
3 _____

NEXT YEAR:

1 _____
2 _____
3 _____

EVERY DAY I WILL:

_____
_____
_____
_____
_____
_____

THE MOST IMPORTANT THING
IN MY LIFE IS:

I WILL BE GRATEFUL FOR:

_____
_____
_____
_____
_____
_____

I WILL NEVER
FORGET THAT:

I PROMISE MYSELF
THAT I:

THE PEOPLE WHO
WILL HELP ME ARE:

WHEN SOMETHING
GOES WRONG, I WILL:

Would You Rather ...?

A fun way to find out more about your likes, dislikes and personal tastes is to answer these quick-fire questions.

Read the questions and then answer with the first thing that comes into your mind. There are no 'right' or 'wrong' answers but you might be surprised by some of your responses!

WOULD YOU RATHER BE A FLOWER OR A TREE?

WOULD YOU RATHER ACT IN A SILLY COMEDY OR A SERIOUS DRAMA?

_____
_____
_____

WOULD YOU RATHER FLY LIKE A BIRD OR SWIM LIKE A DOLPHIN?

_____
_____
_____

WOULD YOU RATHER BE THE CLEVEREST KID IN SCHOOL OR THE SPORTIEST KID IN SCHOOL?

_____
_____
_____

WOULD YOU RATHER BE FAMOUS FOR YOUR DANCING OR YOUR SINGING?

Would you rather wear all red or all blue?

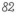

WOULD YOU RATHER TRAVEL 100 YEARS INTO THE FUTURE OR 100 YEARS INTO THE PAST?

_____

_____

_____

WOULD YOU RATHER SPEND THE REST OF YOUR LIFE OUTSIDE OR THE REST OF YOUR LIFE INSIDE?

_____

_____

_____

WOULD YOU RATHER EAT A BOILED EGG OR A SCRAMBLED EGG?

_____

_____

_____

WOULD YOU RATHER BE A PUPPY OR A KITTEN?

_____

_____

_____

Ask your friends and family to write down some more 'would you rather questions' here and then answer them as quickly as you can to discover more about yourself!

Would you rather...

Awesome Achievements

It's easy to reach goals every single day.
It doesn't matter how big or small they are.

Try to keep a list of the things you achieve every day for the next few weeks. You'll soon discover that every day has its own awesome feat!

I have achieved:

. . . .

. . . .

. . . .

. . . .

. . . .

. . . .

When you think of something you'd like to
tick off in the future, make a note of it
here and see if you can do it!

EXAMPLES:

- Surprising a family
  member with
  breakfast in bed

- Passing my
  piano grading

- Learning how to say
  ten words in a
  foreign language

I hope to achieve:

. . . .

. . . .

. . . .

. . . .

. . . .

Talent Star

"Everyone has a hidden talent." — SUSAN GALE

Talent isn't just about being able to sing or dance. It can also mean your strengths, like being really **organized.** List your strengths, your friends' strengths and your family's strengths. Then fill in the stars on the opposite page with the names of those who deserve these labels most.

MY STRENGTHS	MY FRIENDS' STRENGTHS	MY FAMILY'S STRENGTHS

Bravest

MOST HONEST

PRETTIEST

QUIRKIEST

Happiest

SPORTIEST

MOST SERIOUS

CLEVEREST

MOST LOVING

Hardest worker

MOST POLITE

Funniest

BEST HANDWRITING

Life in the Movies

Use the frames below to record your favourite movies of all time, film stars you love to watch and your own dreams of movie stardom. Write, draw pictures or glue in pics from magazines.

- Which movie stars do you admire?
- Which characters do you want to be?
- What are your favourite movies?

- Which movies do you want to see?
- Keep track of everything in this film reel!

Make School Cool

Everyone moans about school sometimes, but why not try to make things better?

Start by listing below the worst thing about school in each section. Then see if you can make suggestions about how to tackle the problem. Finally, choose your best idea and write down what you need to do next, whether it's talking to a teacher, getting your friends on board or making a plan of action.

Lessons

Breaks

Teachers

My Dream Holiday

School holidays are the best! Plan your perfect break here.

Will you stay at home or go away?: . . . .

Boarding Pass

Name

Who is coming with you?

From   To

Transport

Date   Time

PACK YOUR SUITCASE (FOR A WEEK) OR BACKPACK (FOR A DAY) WITH:

. . . .

. . . .

. . . .

. . . .

THE WEATHER WILL BE

(circle two answers):

Boiling hot / freezing cold / warm / cool / rainy / sunny / snowy / windy / cloudy

WHERE WILL YOU BE SLEEPING

(circle one answer or write down your own):

My bed / a hammock on the beach / a posh hotel room / a tent / on the floor / a sleepover with friends / a quiet log cabin in the wilderness / other....

. . . .

Things you'll eat and drink on holiday:

. . . .

. . . .

. . . .

. . . .

. . . .

LIST THE ACTIVITIES YOU HOPE TO DO:

_____

_____

_____

_____

ARE THERE ANY SIGHTS YOU MUST SEE?

. . . .

. . . .

. . . .

. . . .

. . . .

. . . .

. . . .

You could even write a postcard to a friend telling them all about this dream holiday!

Home Is Where the Heart Is

Pretend each of the sections in this house represent an area or room in your home.

Write down your favourite parts of each room. Is it the furniture? Or perhaps it's the view out of the window? Maybe it's what happens in the room rather than the things inside it (like having a bath!) or the colour of the walls?

Now dream big and add one item to each room to make it even better!

Don't forget any outside areas, or you could always include your local park.

Can you and your family help make any of these dream changes come true?

Let Your Mind Wander

"Either write something worth reading or do something worth writing." — BENJAMIN FRANKLIN

Keep track of the thoughts you have when your mind wanders and you might be surprised by what you come up with.

Spot anything unusual during the day? Develop a crazy story around it and you'll have given your brain some exercise!

My Q & A

Every time you have a question you don't know the answer to, note it down here and then make time to research it later and record the answer.

QUESTIONS AND ANSWERS:

Q _____

A _____

Q _____

A _____

Q _____

A _____

Q
_____

A
_____

Q
_____

A
_____

REMINDERS:

1
_____

2
_____

3
_____

WORDS I ALWAYS FORGET HOW TO SPELL:

1 _____   6 _____
2 _____   7 _____
3 _____   8 _____
4 _____   9 _____
5 _____   10 _____

Follow Your Dreams

Make a list of anything and everything you want to do. This list should never end!

And it's never too soon to start ticking things off so why not start today?

Here are some ideas to get you thinking:

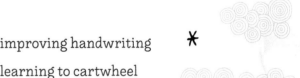

- new food to try
- grades to achieve in school
- new sporting skills
- improving handwriting
- learning to cartwheel
- places to visit
- books to read

ANYTHING AND EVERYTHING I WANT TO DO:

Love Hearts

What or who do you love? Here's a place to write down everything and everyone that makes your heart sing. Turn to it when you're feeling down and you'll soon remember what makes you smile.

Nearest and Dearest

"It's not WHAT we have in our life, but WHO we have our my life that counts." – J. M. LAURENCE

The people around you are there for fun, friendship and support! List everyone you know under the three headings on the next page and stick in photos of some of them. You could also write short descriptions about a few.

MY FAMILY TREE: MY FRIENDSHIP CIRCLE: MY PAW-FECT PETS:

My Famous Family

If you could have a fun celebrity family for a day who would it include and why?

Stick in photos of them from magazines and hashtag reasons why you've chosen them... #sotalented #amazingsportswoman #givesback

FOLLOW •••

My **celeb mum** would be:

♥ ○
♥ ...... LIKES

FOLLOW •••

The **coolest celeb dad** around is:

♥ ○
♥ ...... LIKES

FOLLOW •••

Pick four famous people to be your siblings:

♥ ○
♥ ...... LIKES

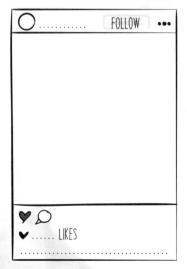

FOLLOW •••

♥ ○
♥ ...... LIKES

FOLLOW •••

♥ ○
♥ ...... LIKES

FOLLOW •••

♥ ○
♥ ...... LIKES

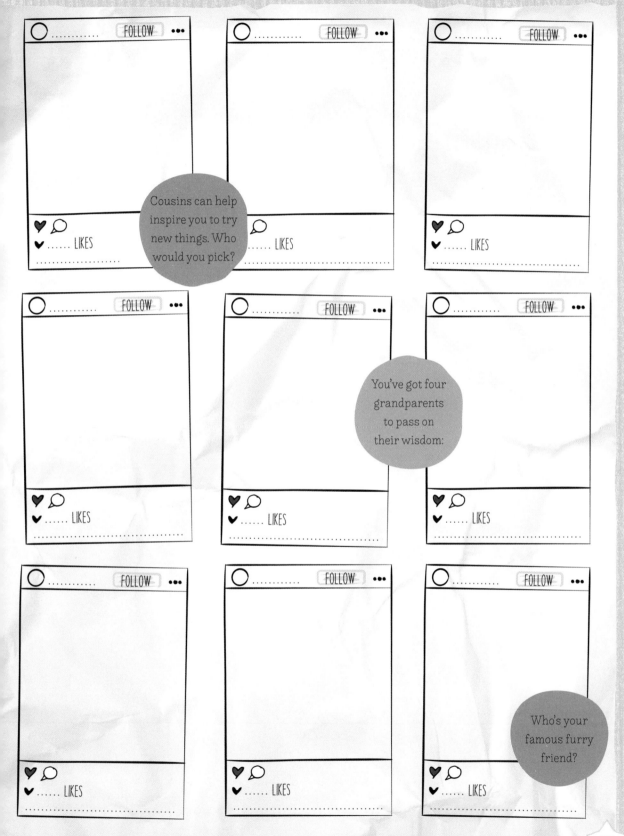

FOLLOW •••

❤ 💬
❤ ...... LIKES

Cousins can help inspire you to try new things. Who would you pick?

You've got four grandparents to pass on their wisdom:

Who's your famous furry friend?

107

Fingerprint Friendship Tree

Collect the fingerprints of your family and friends on this friendship tree. Why not make some friendship flowers too?

Just ask everyone to dip their index (the first) finger in some water-soluble paint or ink and watch your foliage burst into life.

Helping Hand

Everyone needs a helping hand sometimes because you never know what might happen in your exciting life. Without thinking too hard about it, jot down who you would choose to have by your side in these situations.

Find a lost kitten with
....

GET MISTAKEN FOR A POP STAR AND MOBBED BY FANS WITH ....

TRY ON NEW SHOES WITH
....

RESEARCH MY FAMILY HISTORY WITH
....

GO FOR A WALK WITH
....

Have a good cry with
....

TRY OUT NEW HAIRSTYLES WITH ....

MAKE FAIRY CAKES WITH
....

PUT UP PARTY DECORATIONS WITH............................

Go on a round-the-world cruise with
. . . .

PRACTISE DANCE MOVES WITH
. . . .

MEET A TIGER ESCAPED FROM THE ZOO WITH
. . . .

TELL MY DEEPEST SECRETS TO
. . . .

Share the clothes style of
. . . .

DO REALLY HARD HOMEWORK WITH ....

IF I'M POORLY, I LOVE A VISIT FROM
. . . .

GO FOR A PICNIC WITH
. . . .

ON A RAINY DAY, I WANT TO BE WITH
. . . .

GO SURFING WITH
. . . .

BUILD A TREEHOUSE WITH
. . . .

111

Birthday Balloons

Keep a note of everyone's birthdays here and you won't be the person who always forgets!

January

February

March

April

May

July

August

June

October

September

November

December

Gift to Give

Keep a list of present ideas so you have lots to choose from when a birthday or the holiday season arrives.

WHO?	GIFT IDEA

WHO? GIFT IDEA

Activity Days

It's always more exciting to go on an adventure with family or complete an activity with friends than to sit in front of the TV on your own!
So why not plan some fun activities to complete with those you love?

A CRAFT ACTIVITY

WHAT? . . . .   WHO? . . . .

WHERE? . . . .   HOW? . . . .

WHEN? . . . .

AN OUTDOOR ADVENTURE

WHAT? . . . .   WHO? . . . .

WHERE? . . . .   HOW? . . . .

WHEN? . . . .

TRYING SOMETHING NEW

WHAT? . . . .   WHO? . . . .

WHERE? . . . .   HOW? . . . .

WHEN? . . . .

TREAT TIME

WHAT? . . . .   WHO? . . . .

WHERE? . . . .   HOW? . . . .

WHEN? . . . .

Tradition Tracker

What are your family traditions? Do you have traditions with friends as well? Do you have a special breakfast for your birthday? Do you stay up for the New Year? Is there something you always do on family holidays? Write down your five favourite traditions!

Example:

Birthdays always begin with breakfast in bed.

Swap, Switch, Share

"The more we share, the more we have."

– LEONARD NEMOY

It's great to share with friends. But keep track of the music, books and clothes you lend out and you'll avoid any misunderstandings.

ITEM	DATE	BORROWED FROM	DATE RETURNED

ITEM	DATE	LENT TO	DATE RETURNED

You in Review

HOW LONG HAVE YOU TAKEN TO FILL IN THIS JOURNAL:

. . . .

WHICH PAGE DID YOU ENJOY THE MOST: . . . .

WHICH PAGE DID YOU FIND THE HARDEST: . . . .

Try to list a word that best describes you for each letter of the alphabet!

A

B

C

D

E

F

G

H

ME
FROM
A TO Z

I

J

K

L

M

N

O

P

Q

R

S

T

U

V

W

X

Y

Z

My Favourite Me

"Tomorrow is another day." – SCARLETT O'HARA

FROM *GONE WITH THE WIND* BY MARGARET MITCHELL

CONGRATULATIONS! You've almost completed your journal. What have you found out about yourself? Complete the sentences below to sum up what you have learnt and your hopes for the future.

WHAT HAS SURPRISED ME MOST IS DISCOVERING THAT

. . . .

. . . .

. . . .

. . . .

MY FAMILY IS IMPORTANT TO ME BECAUSE

. . . .

. . . .

. . . .

. . . .

THE BEST THING ABOUT MY FRIENDS IS

. . . .

. . . .

. . . .

. . . .

I've realized that school is

. . . .

. . . .

. . . .

. . . .

I WOULDN'T BE WHO I AM TODAY WITHOUT

. . . .

. . . .

. . . .

. . . .

. . . .

. . . .

. . . .

. . . .

I feel more sure than ever that

. . . .

. . . .

. . . .

. . . .

. . . .

. . . .

. . . .

. . . .

. . . .

I'M REALLY LOOKING FORWARD TO

. . . .

. . . .

. . . .

. . . .

. . . .

. . . .

. . . .

. . . .

I'M SO HAPPY I

. . . .

. . . .

. . . .

. . . .

. . . .

. . . .

. . . .

Time Capsule

If you keep this journal forever it will act as a time capsule for your future self!

Decide at which points in your life you should look back at certain pages and hopefully you'll be able to tick them off as the years go by!

Here are some points in time to get you started, but add in some more checkpoints.

CHECKPOINTS

In two months' time on __ / __ / __
I will look back to pages 62–63 and see if I've had a cosy night in

In six months' time on __ / __ / __
I will check pages 66–67 to see if my music tastes have changed

At the start of the new school year on __ / __ / __
I will see if any changes from pages 90–91 have taken place

In a years time on __ / __ / __
I will see which items I've ticked off my list from pages 100–101

In five years' time on __ / __ / __
I will see if my sleep style from pages 18–19 has changed

When I move into my own house on __ / __ / __
I will compare my bedroom to my dream room from pages 22–23

CHECKPOINTS

My Favourite Me

Every day the sun rises and you get a full 24 hours of life to enjoy! What sweet treat has today got in store for you?

Be happy!

Draw a picture of your smiling face below to remind you how great you are, or find a favourite photo and put it in the frame.

THIS IS A CARLTON BOOK

Published in 2018 by Carlton Books Limited, an imprint of the Carlton Publishing Group, 20 Mortimer Street, London W1T 3JW

Text, design and illustration copyright © Carlton Books Limited 2018

A catalogue record for this book is available from the British Library.

ISBN: 978-1-78312-342-1
Printed in Dongguan, China

10 9 8 7 6 5 4 3 2 1

Author: Anna Brett
Executive Editor: Alexandra Koken
Design Manager: Emily Clarke
Design: Rachel Lawston
Production: Emma Smart

Illustrations by Pheobe Leadbeater and Shutterstock